D1457978

The Mystery of the Spotted Band

Based on a Sherlock Holmes story
by Sir Arthur Conan Doyle

Walt Flood

SCHOLASTIC INC.
New York Toronto London Auckland Sydney
Mexico City New Delhi Hong Kong Buenos Aires

Illustrations
Craig Phillips

Text copyright © 2004 by Scholastic Inc.
Illustrations copyright © 2004 by Craig Phillips.
All rights reserved. Published by Scholastic Inc.
Printed in the U.S.A.

ISBN 0-439-67240-6

9   1 0   23   12 11 10 09

Contents

Sherlock Holmes is the world's greatest detective. He sees everything.

1

Meet Sherlock Holmes

My name is Dr. Watson. I work for Sherlock Holmes. He is the world's greatest **detective**.

One morning, Holmes and I were working in his office. The doorbell rang. The doorman told us, "A lady is waiting."

Holmes and I went to meet her. The young lady was sitting in our most

---

detective someone who solves crimes

Sherlock Holmes and I went to meet our visitor, a young lady.

comfortable chair. But she did not look comfortable. She looked scared.

Holmes said to her, "I am Sherlock Holmes. This is my friend, Dr. Watson."

"It's nice to meet you," she said. She was trying to stay calm. But her hands were shaking.

Holmes said, "You must be tired. You took the train early this morning."

"How did you know that?" the lady asked. "Have you been following me?"

"Not at all," said Holmes. "I saw the train ticket in your hand."

I smiled. Holmes's powers of **observation** are very good!

observation the careful watching of someone or something

There has been a murder!
Can Sherlock Holmes find the killer?

Helen's Story

The lady took a deep breath. "My name is Helen," she said. "Ten years ago, my mother died. My sister Julia and I were all alone. We had no one except our stepfather, Bill Hall."

Helen went on. "My mother had lots of money. In her **will**, she asked Bill to take care of us. If he did, he could use

will a letter that says who gets your money and things when you die

"Julia was clutching her throat. She couldn't talk," Helen said.

her money, but only until Julia and I grew up. When we got married, we would each get half the money."

Helen went on. "Bill is a very kind man. He raised Julia and me. We were all very happy together. But then, two years ago, something bad happened.

"It was one week before Julia's

wedding. Julia asked if I ever heard strange whistles in the night. I said no."

Helen continued. "That night, I heard Julia scream! Bill and I ran to her room. The door was locked! I ran to find a key.

"When we opened the door, Julia was screaming, 'The band! The spotted band!'

"Then Julia **clutched** her throat. She tried to talk. But she couldn't. Later, she died. No one knows what killed her."

"Or *who*!" said Holmes.

"My wedding is next week," Helen said. "And last night I heard a whistle!"

Why does Helen think she is in danger?

clutched held tightly

Holmes is on the case.
But can he find any clues?

3

The Search for Clues

"You were smart to come here,"
Holmes said. "Your sister was *murdered!*"

"And I could be next!" Helen cried.

"Don't worry," Holmes said. "I will
solve this **mystery**. Let me start by
inspecting your house. I'll come when
your stepfather isn't home."

Later, we took the train to Helen's

mystery something that's hard to understand
or figure out

inspecting looking at something closely

house. She led us to her sister's room.

Holmes looked around. "No one could have gotten in that night. The windows have bars. And the door was locked!"

Then, Holmes inspected the room. He even looked up at the ceiling. "There!" he cried. "A **vent**! Where does it go?"

"It goes to Bill's room," Helen said.

"That's very interesting," Holmes said.

Next, Helen led us to her stepfather's room. It was almost empty. There was just a chair, a bed, and a wooden box.

"What's in that box?" asked Holmes.

"I don't know," Helen said.

"Helen, tonight Watson and I will stay in your room," Holmes said. "Don't tell your stepfather we are here."

---

vent a small opening that lets air through

4

Death at Midnight

That night, Holmes and I waited in Helen's dark room. We sat very still. Then we heard a whistle. Holmes poked his cane into the vent.

"Look!" he yelled. "Do you see it?"

I didn't see anything. Then a scream came from Helen's stepfather's room. We ran as fast as we could.

The spotted band was wrapped around Mr. Hall's neck!

Helen's stepfather sat in his chair. It was clear that he was dead. A yellow band was wrapped around his neck. The band had brown spots.

"I knew we'd find it," Holmes said. "The spotted band!"

Then the band moved! I gasped. The band was a snake!

"Watch out, Watson!" cried Holmes. "It's a swamp snake! That's the most **poisonous** snake in India!"

The snake turned and looked at us. It slid off of Bill Hall, onto the floor. Holmes looked the snake right in the eyes! Then, the snake slid out the window.

"Oh, no!" I said. "It's on the loose!"

"Don't worry, Watson," said Holmes. "The snake will come back. All we have to do is whistle."

Holmes explained. "Bill Hall trained the snake to come and go when he whistled. He kept the snake in that wooden box."

Holmes went on. "He didn't want to

---

poisonous harmful or deadly

give his stepdaughters their money. So he sent his snake through the vent to kill them! But I knew what to do. I poked that snake with my cane! A scared snake is nobody's friend. Bill Hall's evil plan came back to bite him!"

I went to find Helen. I had good news and bad news. The good news? Holmes had solved the mystery. The bad news? Her stepfather had been a real snake!

Why did Watson call Julia's stepfather a snake?

Glossary

clutched *(verb)* held tightly

detective *(noun)* someone who solves crimes

inspecting *(verb)* looking at something closely *(related words: inspect, inspected)*

mystery *(noun)* something that's hard to understand or figure out

observation *(noun)* the careful watching of someone or something

poisonous *(adjective)* harmful or deadly *(related word: poison)*

vent *(noun)* a small opening that lets air through

will *(noun)* a letter that says who gets your money and things when you die